Teaching Masters and Home Link Masters

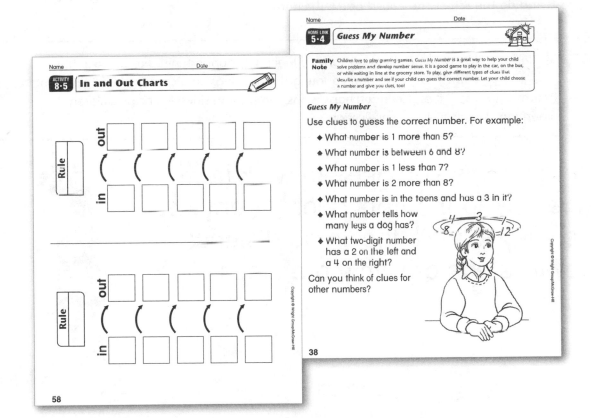

Name _____ Date _____

ACTIVITY 8·5 | **In and Out Charts**

Rule

out

in

Rule

out

in

58

Name _____ Date _____

HOME LINK 5·4 | **Guess My Number**

Family Note Children love to play guessing games. *Guess My Number* is a great way to help your child solve problems and develop number sense. It is a good game to play in the car, on the bus, or while waiting in line at the grocery store. To play, give different types of clues that describe a number and see if your child can guess the correct number. Let your child choose a number and give you clues, too!

Guess My Number

Use clues to guess the correct number. For example:

◆ What number is 1 more than 5?

◆ What number is between 6 and 8?

◆ What number is 1 less than 7?

◆ What number is 2 more than 8?

◆ What number is in the teens and has a 3 in it?

◆ What number tells how many legs a dog has?

◆ What two-digit number has a 2 on the left and a 4 on the right?

Can you think of clues for other numbers?

38

HOME LINK 1·3 | Counting Steps

A Letter to Parents about Home Links

When children are read to, they learn to love books and want to become readers. In a similar way, children develop positive feelings about mathematics by sharing pleasurable experiences as they count, measure, compare, estimate, and discover patterns in everyday life.

Kindergarten Home Links provide a guide to a variety of activities that parents and children can share in a spirit of exploration and enjoyment, much as they share interesting stories.

The reward for young children is that mathematics will not be a puzzling abstraction but will make sense to them as part of their real world.

When your child brings home a Home Link, take a moment to look at the Family Note. Then, together with your child, read and do the activity described below the note.

Family Note Children enjoy counting things. Be on the lookout for opportunities to practice this skill. You'll be pleasantly surprised how counting things brings about many playful and productive mathematics activities. Counting hops, skips, jumps, and sidesteps helps children develop counting skills as well as coordination.

Count the steps you need to walk from the sidewalk to the front door (or any two places). Try to walk the same distance with fewer steps or with more steps.

Get into the counting habit!
When you take a walk, try hopping, skipping, jumping, or sidestepping a certain number of times.

Name _____   Date _____

Numbers All Around

Family Note In this activity, children become more aware of numerals all around them, as well as the varied uses of numbers. Look around and encourage your child to notice numbers in your home. Talk with them about what the numbers represent and how they are used.

Look for numbers around your house.

Where did you find the most? In your bedroom? In the kitchen?

Where else did you find numbers?

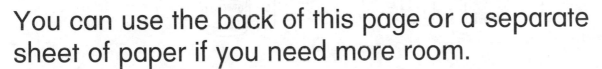

Draw a picture of some of the things with numbers that you found.

You can use the back of this page or a separate sheet of paper if you need more room.

3

Measuring Capacity

HOME LINK 1·7

> **Family Note** The process of filling containers and comparing how much each can hold gives your child the opportunity to experiment with the measurement of capacity without worrying about exact answers.
>
> For this activity, make sure that the containers are nonbreakable. Bath time provides an excellent opportunity to experiment and play with containers of all shapes and sizes.

Collect some containers that are different shapes and sizes, such as cottage cheese cartons, plastic bottles, and juice containers.

Use the containers to pour water back and forth. Try to find out which container holds the most, which container holds the least, and which containers hold about the same amount.

HOME LINK
1·11

Sorting Groceries

Family Note	Sorting helps children develop the ability to examine a variety of items and to develop classification categories into which they can be grouped.

Before unpacking a grocery bag, try to guess how many items are inside it. Then count to see how close you were.

Sort the grocery items into groups. Explain why you put certain items together.

Can you think of a different way to sort the items?

HOME LINK 2·1 *I Spy* with Geometry

Play *I Spy* with someone. Pick an object that you can see. Give a clue about the shape of the object. The other person guesses which object you are describing. Begin with easy clues and then give some harder ones.

Examples:

- "I spy something that is round."

- "I spy something that is round and has two hands."

- "I spy something that is a rectangle and has rectangular buttons."

Take turns trying to stump each other.

HOME LINK 2·5 Patterns All Around

Look outdoors and in your home for objects that have patterns. Choose your favorite pattern to draw and bring to school to share.

Triangle Patterns in a Radiator Cover

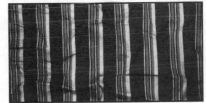

Patterns in a Striped Blanket

ACTIVITY 2·7 Tactile Number Strokes, Part 1

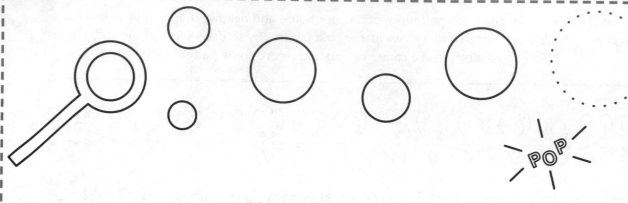

Bubbles (circular strokes)

Clouds (curved strokes)

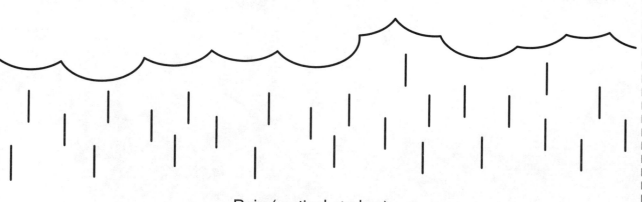

Rain (vertical strokes)

ACTIVITY 2·7

Tactile Number Strokes, Part 2

Lines (horizontal strokes)

Slides (diagonal strokes)

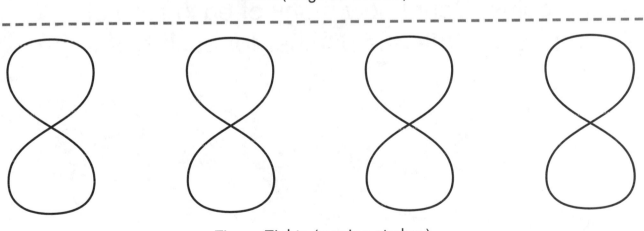

Figure Eights (curving strokes)

Name _____ Date _____

Family Note Children will learn about coins and their values by handling them, sorting them, matching them, helping you pay for items, and collecting change. Look for opportunities for your child to help you handle and use real money. Allow your child to empty a coin purse, search your pockets, or look under the couch cushions to find coins at home. Have him or her practice matching and sorting the coins, taking care to notice both sides of the coins.

Be a Coin Detective! Draw a picture of all the coins you find around your house.

Sort the coins. Count how many of each type of coin you have. Write the number for each type of coin.

ACTIVITY 2·9   Blank Number Board

0									
1									
2									
3									
4									
5									
6									
7									
8									
9									
10									

HOME LINK 2·13 | **Penny Jar**

Family Note A penny jar provides great mathematics opportunities! Have family members add spare pennies at the end of each day. Count the pennies together once a week to reinforce the counting skills we are working on in school. As the penny collection grows, family members can estimate how many pennies are in the jar before counting them. Estimation is not just guessing. It is using what you know to make a "smart guess."

Start a penny jar to collect your family's pennies.

Once a week, estimate how many coins are in the jar:

Take a small handful of pennies and count them. Compare the number in your hand with the number in the penny jar. How many pennies do you think are in the jar? Count the pennies in the jar and record the number. How close was your estimate?

How many pennies do you think will be in your jar next week? Keep track of how the number changes.

ACTIVITY 3·1

Number Book (0)

Name

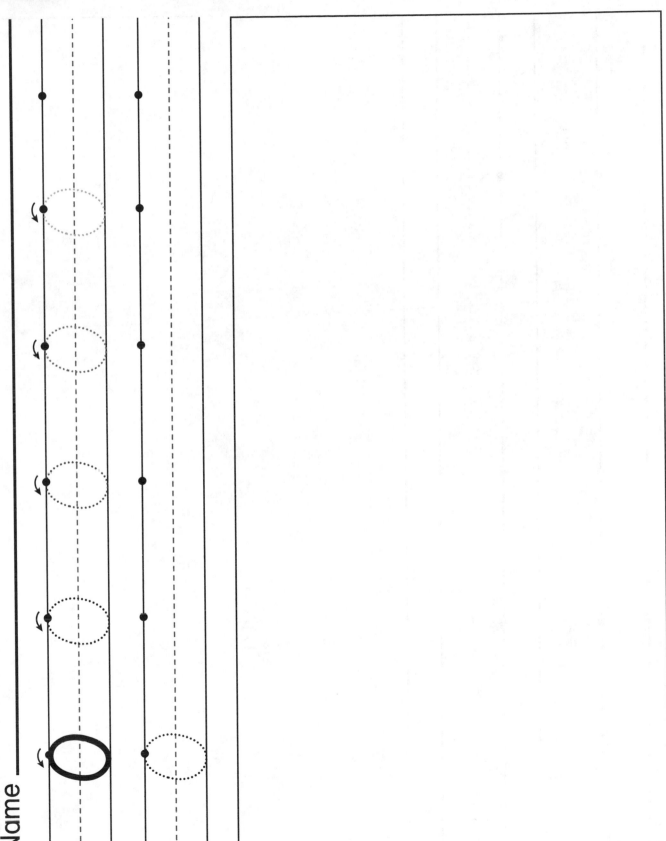

ACTIVITY 3·1 Number Book (1)

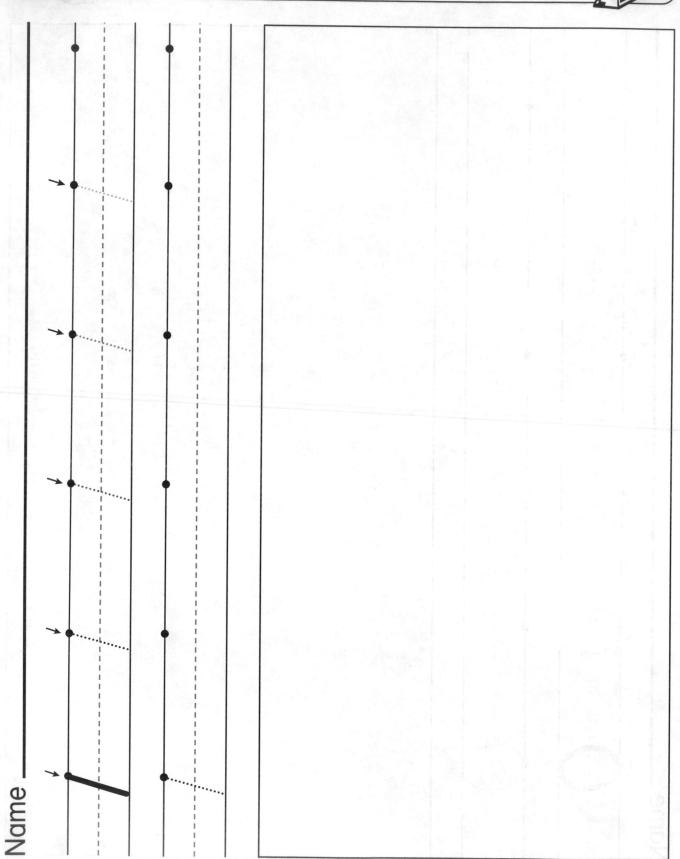

ACTIVITY 3·1

Number Book (2)

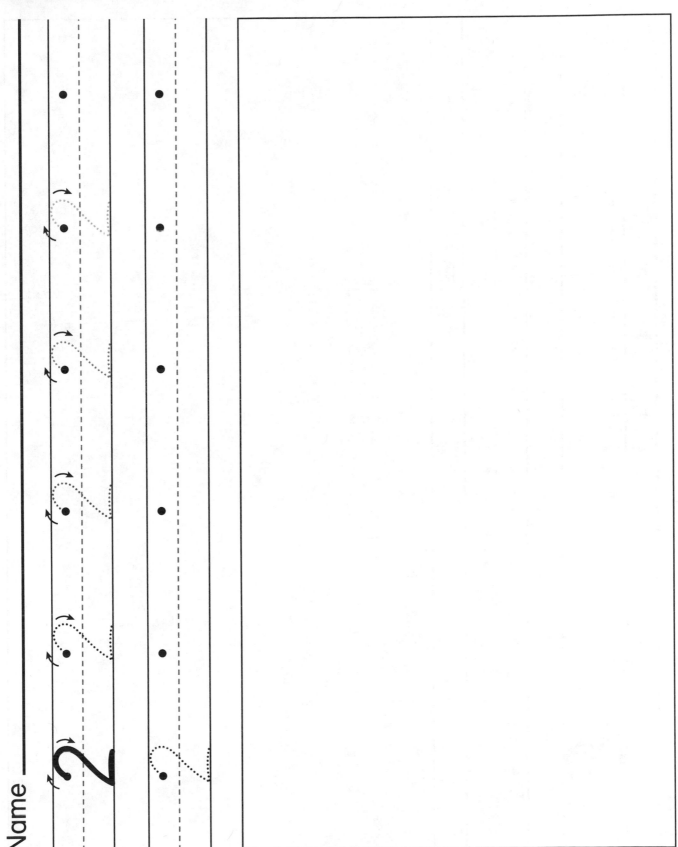

Name

ACTIVITY 3·1

Number Book (3)

3

Name

ACTIVITY 3·1 | Number Book (4)

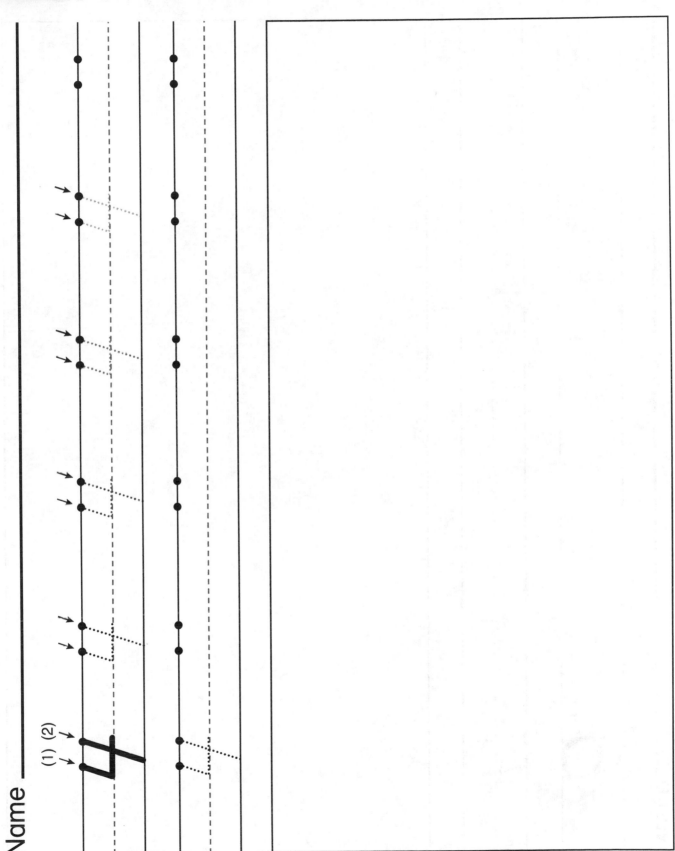

ACTIVITY 3·1 | **Number Book (5)**

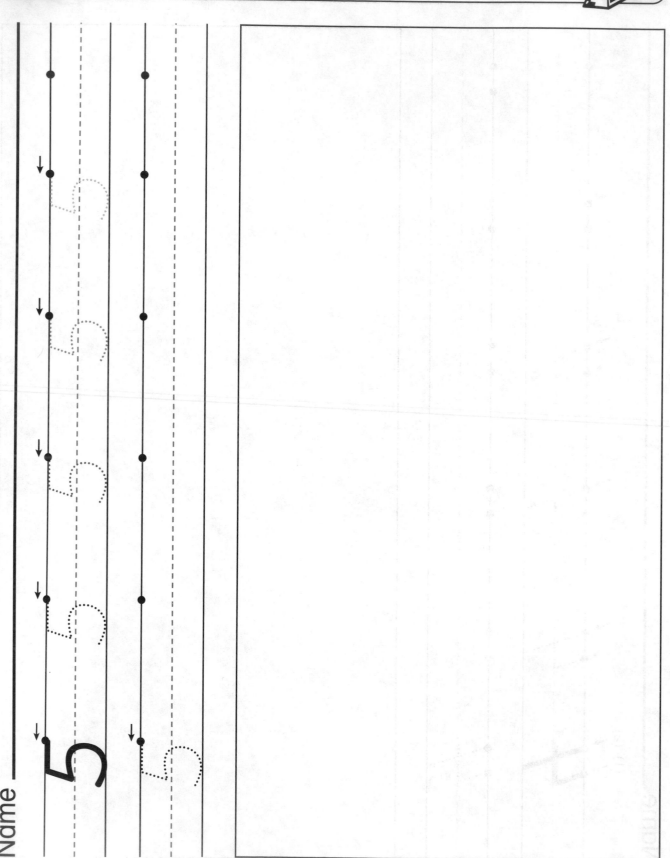

Name

ACTIVITY 3·1 | **Number Book (6)**

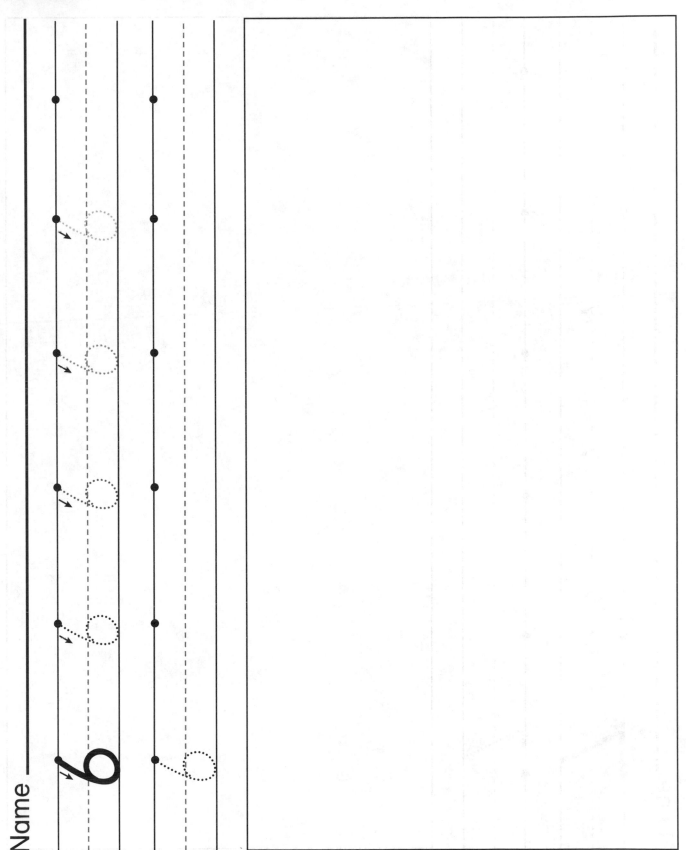

Name _____

ACTIVITY 3·1 **Number Book (7)**

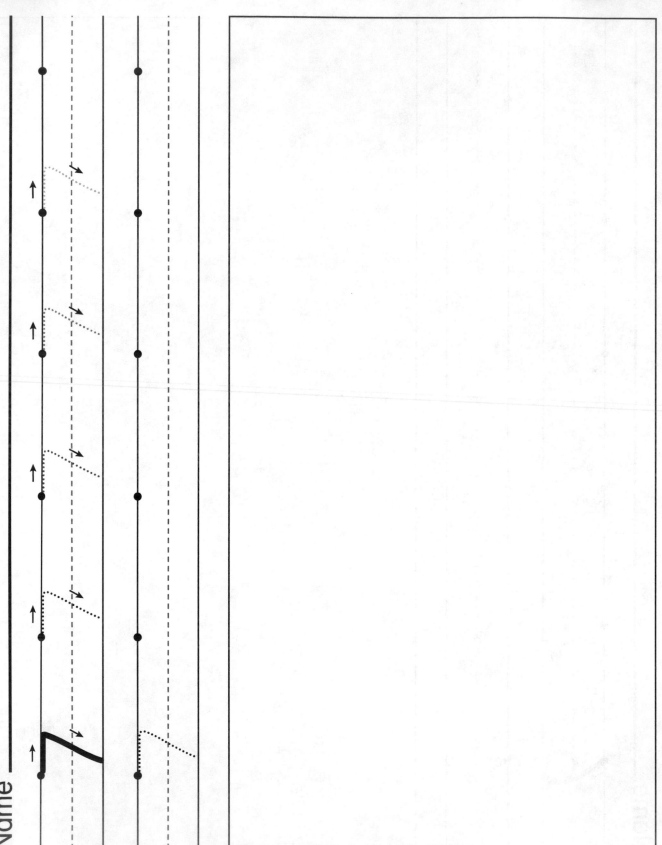

Name

ACTIVITY 3·1   **Number Book (8)**

Name _____

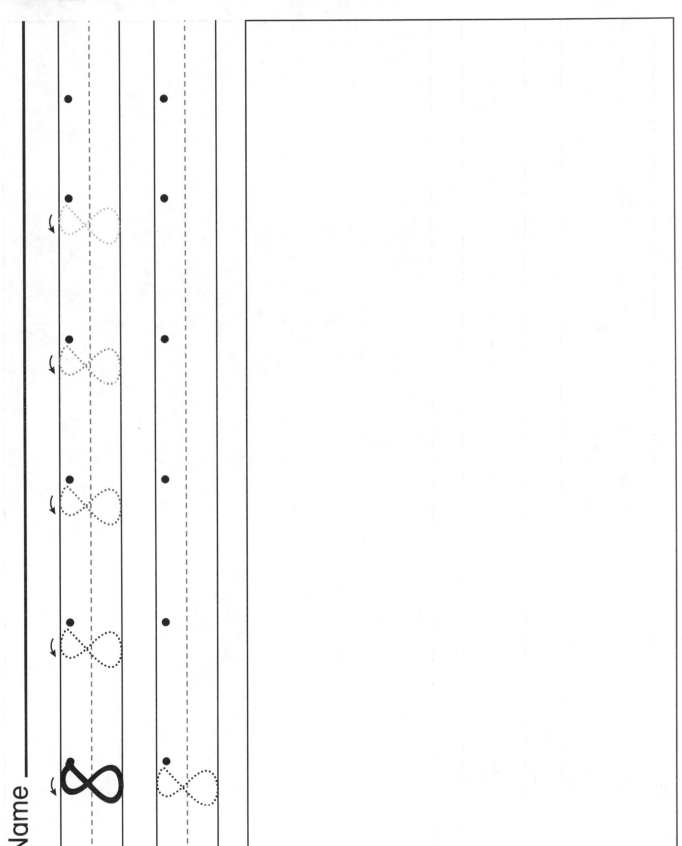

Name

ACTIVITY 3·1 | Number Book (9)

Number Book (10)

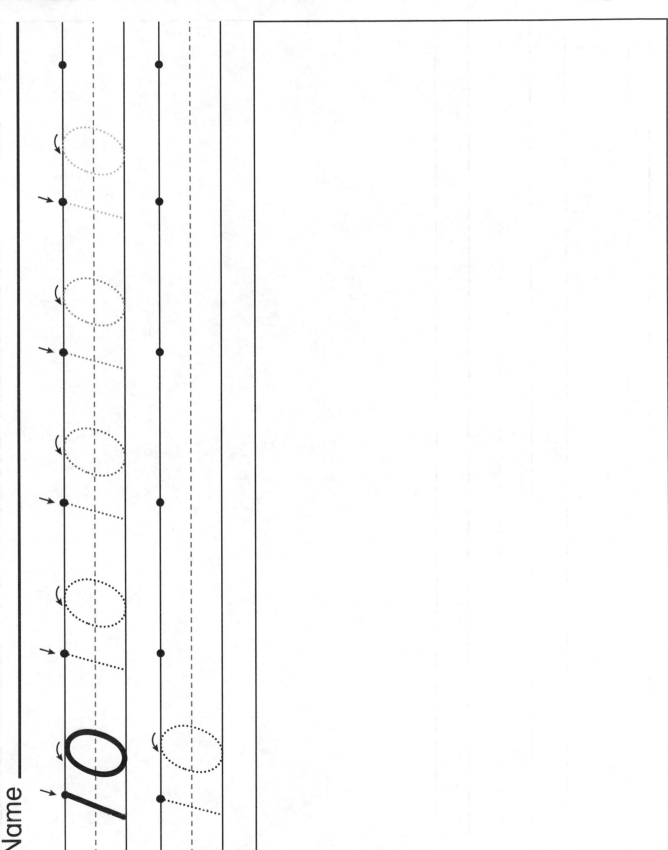

Name

ACTIVITY 3·1

Number Book (blank)

Name _____

HOME LINK 3·2 | **Shape and Color Patterns**

You can make patterns with food.

Use cereal and crackers that have different shapes and colors.

Use cereal or pasta with holes to make a necklace or bracelet.

String the cereal or pasta (or both) in a pattern on yarn. Make shape patterns, color patterns, or both.

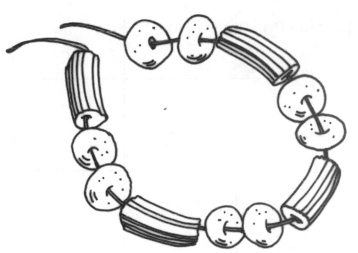

Glue your patterns on paper if you don't want a necklace or bracelet.

(Do not eat these patterns!)

ACTIVITY 3·3 | **Roll and Record**

1	**2**	**3**	**4**	**5**	**6**

ACTIVITY 3·3 **Roll and Record (Number Writing)**

1	2	3	4	5	6
1	2	3	4	5	6
1	2	3	4	5	6
1	2	3	4	5	6
1	2	3	4	5	6
1	2	3	4	5	6
1	**2**	**3**	**4**	**5**	**6**

HOME LINK 3·6 Monster Squeeze

Family Note Games are a wonderful way for children to practice mathematics skills. *Monster Squeeze* is a game that reinforces number recognition and the concepts of greater and less. Directions are provided below, but let your child take the lead in teaching you the game.

Materials Two monsters and a 1–10 number line.

Players 2

Skill Compare numbers

Object of the Game To guess the mystery number

Directions

1. Player 1 places one monster at each end of the number line, facing each other. The same player chooses a mystery number between 1 and 10 and writes it on a piece of paper.

2. Player 2 guesses a number.

3. Player 1 says whether the number guessed is too low or too high and covers the number with a monster. (The left monster covers the number if the guess was too low. The right monster covers the number if the guess was too high.)

Example: If the mystery number is 6 and the guess is 3, the left-hand monster moves up the number line to cover the 3. If the guess is 8, the right-hand monster moves down the number line to cover the 8.

4. Players keep guessing and moving the monsters until the mystery number is guessed, or "squeezed," between the monsters!

Cut out the monsters and the number line.

Use them to teach someone in your family to play *Monster Squeeze.*

| 1 | 2 | 3 | 4 | 5 | 6 | 7 | 8 | 9 | 10 |

HOME LINK 3·7 | **Measuring in Penny Lengths**

Family Note   Units of measurement originated from things familiar to people. Using objects around the house to measure items is one way to help children understand the concept of nonstandard measurement and to practice measuring techniques.

Measure the length of a shoe using pennies instead of inches. Then, measure someone else's shoe using pennies. Did it take more pennies or fewer pennies?

Now measure another object, such as a pencil or a floor tile, using pennies.

Find something else to measure with—like raisins or a small toy.

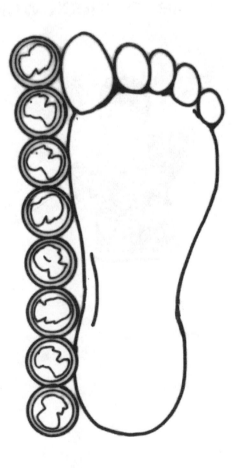

29

HOME LINK 3·12 | Heavier or Lighter?

Family Note   In school, we have started to talk about different kinds of measurement, such as volume, length, and weight. Children will find many ways to explore measurement at home and elsewhere. Encourage the development of measurement skills by helping your child find and recognize the many uses of measurement in everyday life. Model the correct usage of words and tools to describe and compare sizes, amounts, and weights of different things. (We've been learning about pan balances in school.)

Compare the weights of two objects by holding one in each hand.

Can you tell which one is heavier? Lighter?

Draw a picture on the back of this paper that shows which object felt heavier and which object felt lighter. How did your arms look?

What tools could you use to check which object weighs more?

HOME LINK 3·15 Counting Fingers

Count all of the fingers in your family.

Count by 10s. (Don't forget yourself!)

Count by 1s to double check.

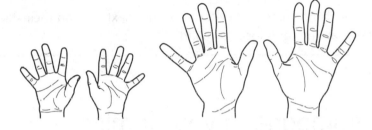

Draw the fingers of all the people in your family.

Try to write the number of fingers.

(It might be a big number. Ask someone for help if you need it.)

What else could you count by 10s?

(Hint: What do you put in a shoe?)

31

HOME LINK 4·2

Top-It

Family Note *Top-It* reinforces number recognition and helps children learn to compare two numbers to decide which one is greater or less. (You may remember this game as War.)

Materials   Number cards from school or a deck of cards *(Make a number deck using index cards) 1-10 11-20 20-?*

Players   2

Skill   Compare numbers

Object of the Game Collect the higher number of cards

Directions

1. Shuffle a deck of cards and then divide it between two players, turning the cards facedown on the table.

2. Players turn over their top cards and read the numbers aloud.

3. The player with the greater number keeps both cards.

If both players get the same number, they turn over the next card on their stacks until one player wins and takes all the cards for that round.

Play *Top-It* with someone in your family.

Creating Patterns

Collect different kinds and sizes of objects.

Look for buttons and coins and lids from juice bottles and soda bottles.

Use the objects to make patterns.

Try to describe the pattern to someone.

See if someone can extend your pattern.

Ask someone to create a pattern for you to extend.

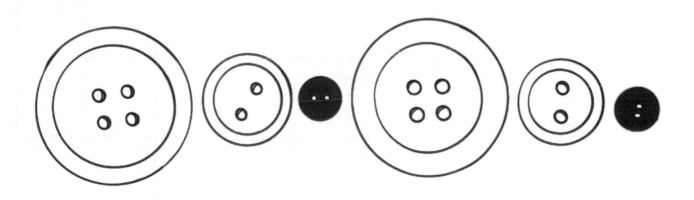

ACTIVITY 4·8 **Dice-Throw Grid**

2							
3							
4							
5							
6							
7							
8							
9							
10							
11							
12							

ACTIVITY 4·9

Symmetry Snowflake

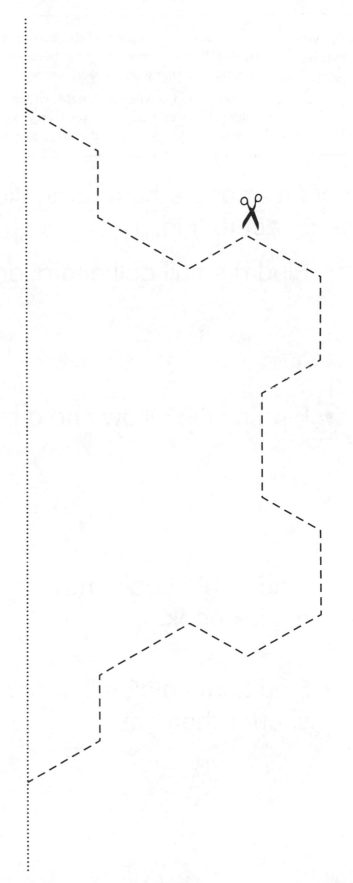

HOME LINK 4·13 **Treasure Hunt**

> **Family Note** *Attributes* describe the physical characteristics of an object, such as its size, color, and shape. Your child has been identifying attributes and sorting by attributes in school. These skills lay a foundation for later work in geometry and algebra.
>
> Help your child become comfortable with describing and organizing objects according to multiple characteristics. A treasure hunt is a great way to encourage your child to use descriptive words to identify the size, color, and shape of objects around your home.

Have a treasure hunt using clues to describe the object to find.

- Find a small ball and a large ball.

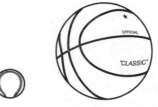

- Find a little pillow and a big pillow.

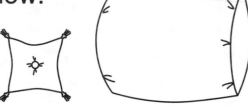

- Find a thin book and a thick book.

- Find something taller than you and something shorter than you.

100th Day Project

Family Note   Our class has been adding one number for each school day to our Growing Number Line. The 100th day of school is coming up soon, and it will be a major celebration!

One of the things we will do to celebrate is create a 100 Museum that will contain collections of 100 things brought in by each child. Children have been thinking about things they might collect, such as a chain of 100 paper clips, a collection of 100 baseball cards, a necklace with 100 beads, or a building made from 100 blocks. We have been talking about ways to count the collections without losing track of the numbers. Making groups of 10 is a good way to count and display the objects.

Children may need a little help gathering materials, but they should be able to do most of the work themselves. Your child can bring in his or her collection as soon as it is ready. We look forward to a rich mathematical day!

Start a collection of 100 objects.

Count your objects and arrange them in whatever way you like.

Bring your 100th Day Project to school by

_____.

HOME LINK 5·4

Guess My Number

Guess My Number

Use clues to guess the correct number. For example:

◆ What number is 1 more than 5?

◆ What number is between 6 and 8?

◆ What number is 1 less than 7?

◆ What number is 2 more than 8?

◆ What number is in the teens and has a 3 in it?

◆ What number tells how many legs a dog has?

◆ What two-digit number has a 2 on the left and a 4 on the right?

Can you think of clues for other numbers?

ACTIVITY 5·7 **Standard Foot-Long Foot**

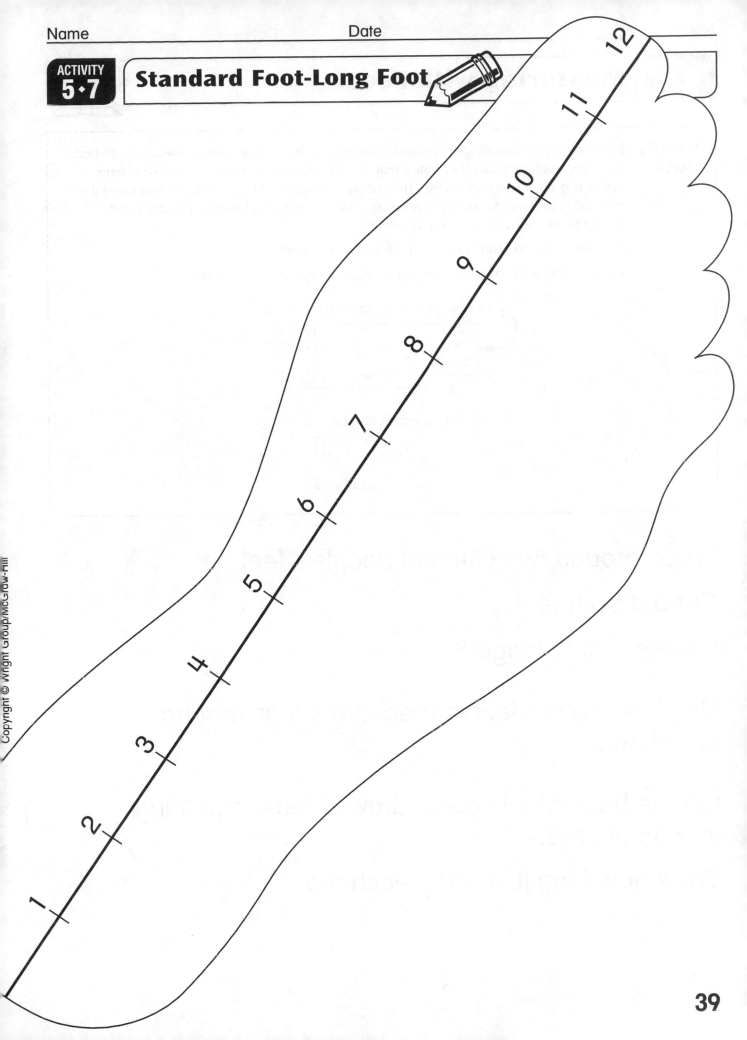

HOME LINK 5·7 | **Measuring with Feet**

Family Note Before children measure with standard measuring tools, they can learn to measure with body parts, such as feet. When they notice that this method produces different measurements—depending on whose foot is used—they begin to understand why standard measurement units are important. As your child measures with foot cutouts at home, reinforce good measurement techniques, especially by

◆ lining up the measuring tool with the end of the object being measured,

◆ laying the tool end-to-end (without overlaps or gaps) as they measure.

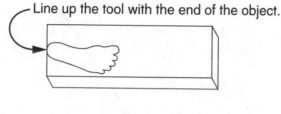

Line up the tool with the end of the object.

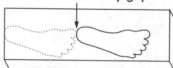

Do not leave any gaps.

Trace around two different people's feet.

Cut out both feet.

Whose foot is longer?

Use both cutout feet to measure things around your house.

On the back of this page, draw at least one thing you measured.

Write how long it is using each foot.

ACTIVITY 5·9 | **How Did You Come to School? Tally**

Cut out the pictures below for your tally chart.

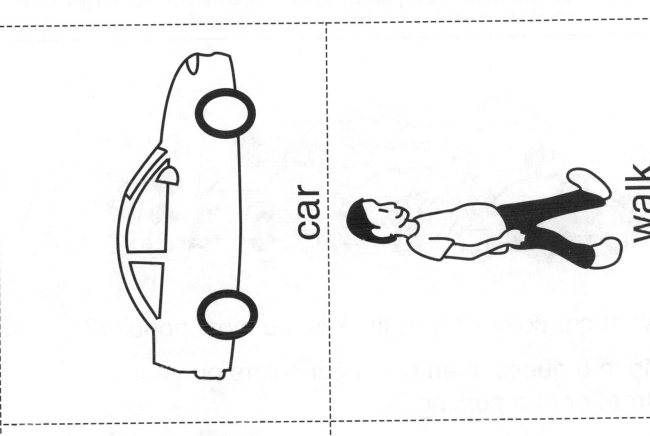

car

walk

bus

bicycle

HOME LINK 5·9 | **Car Color Tally**

Family Note Collecting data helps children count, sort, compare, and record information. In school, we are learning about using tally marks to record data. Explore data collection with your child by using tally marks to record the color of cars in your neighborhood.

What car color do you think is the most popular?

Make a guess, then count car colors on your street or in a parking lot.

Use tally marks to record as you count.

What did you find out?

ACTIVITY 5·14 | **Cookie Survey Tally Chart**

Which kind of cookie do you like best?

chocolate chip	
peanut butter	
sugar	

HOME LINK 6·3 **Solid Shape Museum**

Family Note Manipulating, exploring, and discussing 3-dimensional objects helps children learn the names of these objects and build spatial sense. Many familiar objects are common 3-dimensional geometric shapes: balls are spheres and dice are cubes, for example. Children have been learning about 2-dimensional and 3-dimensional shapes and noticing shapes all around them. At home, encourage your child to think about 2- and 3-dimensional shapes as he or she looks for objects to place in our classroom Shape Museum.

Look around your home for objects that have 3-dimensional geometric shapes.

See if you can find examples like these:

Sphere: ball, globe
Cube: dice, square box
Cylinder: can of food
Cone: ice cream cone, party hat
Rectangular prism: cereal box, book

Bring in a few objects to add to our classroom Shape Museum.

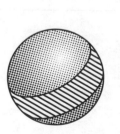

sphere   rectangular prism   cylinder

HOME LINK 6·8

Collecting and Trading Coins

> **Family Note** You may have started to collect pennies in a family Penny Jar. If so, you probably have a lot of pennies by now! Start adding nickels and dimes to your jar so you can do the activities described below. Your coin collection is an excellent tool for developing mathematical skills such as counting, sorting, coin recognition, and coin exchange.

Empty the coins from your jar and sort the coins.

Count the pennies. Can you think of a good way to keep track of the total?

Make piles of 10 pennies and count the pennies by 10s.

Can you trade one pile of 10 for another coin? What is the name of this coin? Trade some more pennies for dimes.

10 *20*

Make piles of 5 pennies and count the pennies by 5s. Can you trade one pile of 5 for another coin? What is the name of this coin? Trade some more pennies for nickels.

45

HOME LINK 6·12 | **Reading the Calendar**

Look at your calendar to find answers to the following questions:

◆ How many days are in this month?

◆ How many Wednesdays? Fridays? Sundays?

◆ What day of the week is the first? The fifth?

◆ What is today's date?

◆ How many days are left in this month?

◆ Are there any birthdays, holidays, or special days this month? When are they? Circle or mark them on your calender.

HOME LINK 6·14 | Counting by 2s, 5s, and 10s

Counting by 2s

Look for things around your house that come in pairs (socks, shoes, eyes, and mittens). You can count the pairs by 2s.

Counting by 5s

Count the fingers in your family by 1s. Now count them by 5s. Count the nickels in your money jar by 5s, too.

Counting by 10s

You've had lots of practice counting fingers by 10s. Now count toes. Try to count dimes by 10s, too.

ACTIVITY 6·15 | **Showing Patterns with Symbols**

Think of a movement pattern.

Draw symbols to show your pattern.

Show your pattern to someone.

Tell what the symbols mean.

Have him or her follow the pattern.

HOME LINK 6·16 **Half Snacks**

Family Note Meals and snacks provide opportunities for mathematical learning. At school we have been learning about the concept of *half*. As you talk with your child about halves, reinforce the idea that two halves of something must be the same or equal size. Children should try to make halves of **collections** of food items (such as pretzels in a bag) and halves of **single** food items (such as a sandwich, orange, or cookie).

Make a **half snack.**

Make a sandwich and cut it in half. Are the two sides equal?

Ask someone to cut an apple and give you half. Check that the piece you got is the same size as the other piece.

Make a pile of raisins or chips. Divide the pile in half. Take one pile and give the other one to someone at home.

What other foods could you divide in half? Try it.

Name _____   Date _____

Class Collection

Family Note   Today we began a class collection of objects that we will use in school for number activities such as counting, keeping records, and grouping by 5s and 10s. The children voted to collect _____. Please help your child find items to contribute to our collection. We will build the class collection for at least the next week or two.

Look around your house for _____.

Count how many you have and put them in a bag.

Bring your bag to school to add to the class collection.

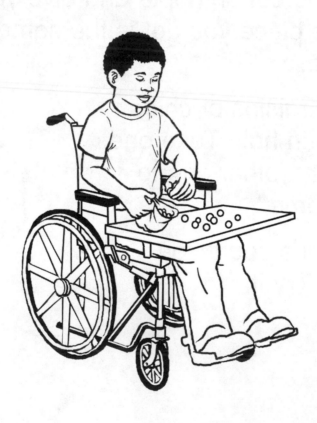

Name _____   Date _____

HOME LINK 7·4 | Building Geometric Shapes

Build shapes and structures with toothpicks and marshmallows or gumdrops.

Begin with flat 2-dimensional shapes, and then try building 3-dimensional shapes such as cubes, pyramids, and prisms.

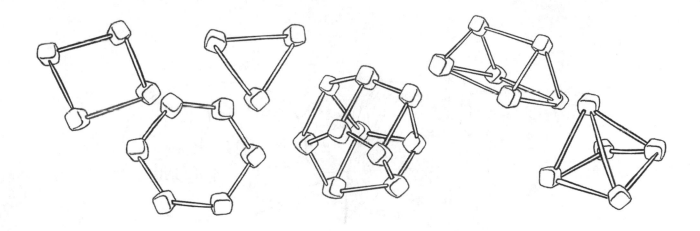

Bring one or two of your shapes to school.

HOME LINK 7·7

Counting Up and Back

Family Note In addition to counting actual objects, children enjoy the rhythm and pattern of reciting numbers in order. As children develop their oral counting skills, they also become aware of the patterns and structure of our number system. Encourage children to count as far as they can and give subtle hints or prompts to help them count a little higher each time. Children enjoy seeing how high they can go, and they gain a real sense of power when they can start counting from any number.

Practice counting to 100 and beyond.

Start counting at 1. Then start at another number such as 15, 27, or 45.

Count backward sometimes too.

- Count down to 0 like a rocket liftoff, a timer, or a microwave.

- Try counting down from a teen or higher number.

HOME LINK 7·9 | Collections of Number Names

Family Note In school we are working on the idea that numbers can be shown in different ways. For example, the number 6 can be shown as 5 and 1; 4 and 2; 3 and 3; and 6 and 0. This is a *name collection* for the number 6. Dividing a collection of objects into groups helps children to understand that the total stays the same even though the number in each group changes. This is an important concept for more advanced mathematics that children will explore later.

How many are in your family? _____
(Include pets and grandparents or other family members if you wish.)

What are some different ways to group the members of your family?

Draw them on the back of this page.

1

4

3

2

53

HOME LINK 7·14 | # Comparing Numbers

Family Note
In school, children are encouraged to notice and think about the numbers all around them. You can help your child find and use numbers in a grocery store sales flyer or newspaper advertisement. Help children compare the prices on the flyer and order the price numbers from smallest to largest.

Look for numbers in a sales flyer.

Cut out numbers that tell the prices of different kinds of food.

Put the numbers in order from smallest to largest.

Tell which number is the highest and which is the lowest.

Carrots
39¢

Canned
Peas
75¢

Name _____   Date _____

How Long Is an Hour?

Family Note   The concept of passing time is difficult for young children. Hours, minutes, and seconds are confusing; children usually do not have a good sense of how long each time interval is or how long things take to do. Help your child make connections between familiar activities and the time spent on those activities. When you tell your child something is happening in 5 minutes (or some other interval), try to stick to that interval to help develop his or her sense of time. Use opportunities such as cooking or television viewing to use timing devices to measure or track intervals of time.

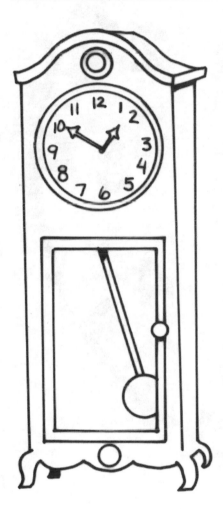

Think of things you can do in about 1 hour.

Ask a family member to help you figure out how long things take to do. Track the time it takes to get to school, bake cookies, go grocery shopping, or watch a television show.

Set a timer for 1 hour. Draw or write down everything you do before the timer rings. You can use the back of this sheet or another piece of paper.

Bring your list to school to add to our class list.

ACTIVITY 8·3 | Paper Clock

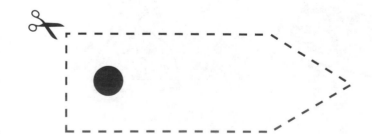

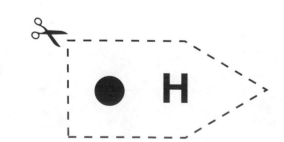

ACTIVITY 8·5 **Function Machine**

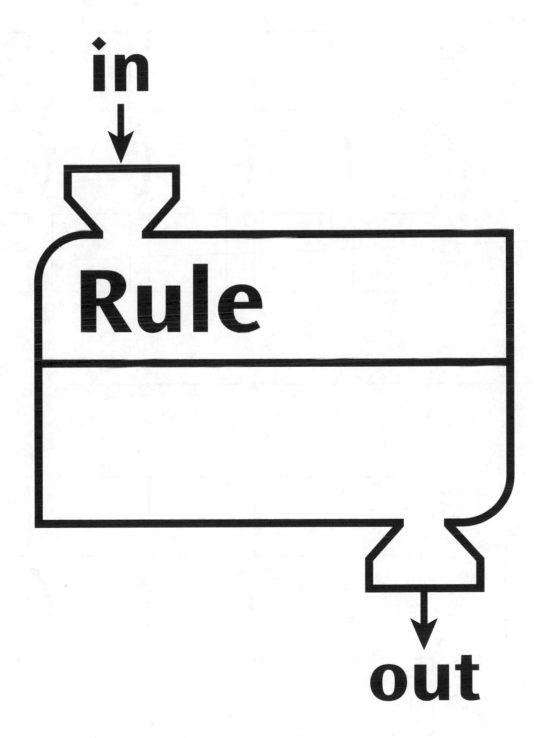

in

Rule

out

ACTIVITY 8·5 | In and Out Charts

Rule

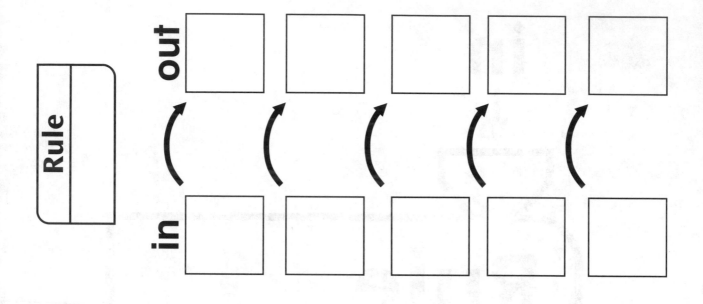

out

in

Rule

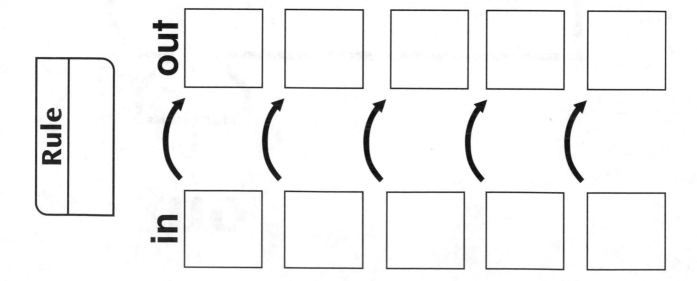

out

in

Name _____ Date _____

Collecting Data about Mail

> **Family Note** Observing and collecting data gives children the opportunity to count and compare numbers and to think about how numbers are used to give information. Help your child collect data about the mail you receive for one week. Also help him or her correctly use and count tallies on the chart.

Ask someone to help you make a tally chart like the one below. Make a tally mark in the correct row for each piece of mail that comes during the week. At the end of the week, count your tallies to find out how much of each type of mail your family received.

How much mail did your family get in a week?

Which was the most common type of mail?

Which was the least common type of mail?

TYPE	OUR MAIL
PERSONAL LETTERS	//
BUSINESS / BILLS	̶H̶H̶ //
MAGAZINES	//
ADS / JUNK MAIL	̶H̶H̶ ̶H̶H̶ //

59

HOME LINK 8·8   Exploring Coins

Family Note Children are familiar with money transactions, but many children are unable to distinguish between coins, understand a coin's value, or realize that a coin of greater value can be exchanged for several coins of lesser value. To build your child's familiarity with money, empty your coin purse or pocket and have fun exploring pennies, nickels, dimes, and quarters together.

Ask someone at home to empty a purse or pocket. Explore the coins with them and think about these questions:

- How many pennies are there? Nickels? Dimes? How many coins all together?

- Which coin is the biggest? Which is the smallest? The thickest? The thinnest?

- How many pennies equal a nickel? How many pennies equal a dime?

- Do you think all the coins add up to more or less than $1?

- What else do you notice about the coins?

HOME LINK 8·11 | **Timing Yourself**

Family Note As children learn about time, they may have difficulty understanding how long a minute is. In this activity, your child will think about what he or she is able to do in a minute.

Guess how long a minute lasts. Ask someone to help you check the clock and tell you when to start timing. Clap your hands when you think a minute has passed. How close were you?

How many sit-ups, leg raises, arm raises, or jumping jacks can you do in one minute?

Think of other activities that you can do in one minute. Can you touch your toes 10 times, do 5 jumping jacks, and spin around 3 times in one minute?

HOME LINK 8·14 | **Telling Number Stories**

Family Note Help your child become a problem solver. Keep in mind that children need to talk about their ideas and have someone listen and offer encouragement. We have been telling number stories in school. Take turns telling and solving number stories with your child. Children enjoy number stories that relate to their own lives.

Tell a "5" number story (a story with 5 as the answer) to someone in your family. Use people in your family as characters in your story.

Tell a number story about something in the kitchen.

Example: We have 1 can of tuna, but we need 4 for this recipe. How many more cans do we need to buy?

Ask someone in your family to make up number stories for you to solve!

ACTIVITY 8·15 Level Pan Balance

Draw what you put in both sides of your pan balance to make it **level**.

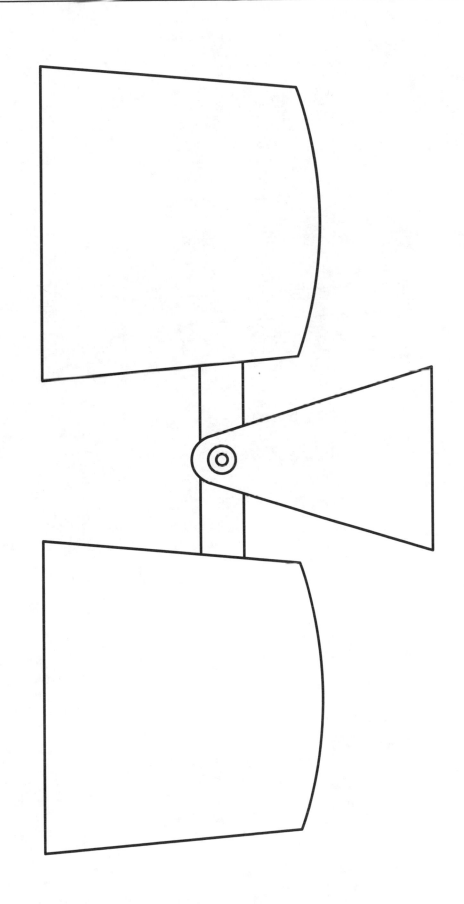

Project Masters

Name _____ Date _____

PROJECT 6 — Mapping a Room

Make a map of a room where you spend lots of time. Use the back of this paper as your map. You will need tape or glue to attach the rectangle your teacher gave you.

1. First, draw any doors and windows.

2. Then, attach the cutout rectangle to show an important thing in the room, such as a bed, a table, or a sofa.

3. Add other furniture and objects that are in the room. (You can draw them or attach cutout paper shapes.)

4. Label some of the things on your map.

5. Bring your room map to school to share with the class.

79

Name _____ Date _____

PROJECT 2 — Body Measures at Home

Try the following measurement activities.

Family Heights

1. Mark the heights of family members on a doorframe.

2. Measure again in the same place every few months.

3. Has there been a change?

Add initials and the date to each mark to help you remember.

Weight

1. Estimate how much you weigh.

2. Measure your weight on a bathroom scale.

3. A young beaver weighs about 40 pounds. Is that more or less than you weigh?

4. Put objects on the scale to make a collection that weighs the same as you.

67

PROJECT 1 | **Class Telephone Book**

Name: _____

Telephone Number: <u>**1**– _____ – _____ – _____</u>

(area code)

PROJECT 2 | Body Measures at Home

Try the following measurement activities.

Family Heights

1. Mark the heights of family members on a doorframe.

2. Measure again in the same place every few months.

3. Has there been a change?

Add initials and the date to each mark to help you remember.

Weight

1. Estimate how much you weigh.

2. Measure your weight on a bathroom scale.

3. A young beaver weighs about 40 pounds. Is that more or less than you weigh?

4. Put objects on the scale to make a collection that weighs the same as you.

PROJECT 3 | **Shisima Directions**

Materials
☐ gameboard
☐ 2 sets of 3 markers (Each set should be a different color.)

Players   2

Skill   Problem-solving

Object of the Game To get 3 water bugs in a row

Directions

1. Players decide who will move from the black bugs and who will move from the white bugs on the gameboard.

2. Players put their markers on the correct color bugs. Each marker is a bug.

3. Players take turns moving one space along a line to the next place where the lines meet. (One place is in the middle of the water.) *No jumping over another bug!*

4. Players try to get their 3 bugs in a row, crossing the middle of the water. The first player with his or her 3 bugs in a row is the winner.

5. If no one can make a new move, it's a tie.

PROJECT 3

Shisima Gameboard

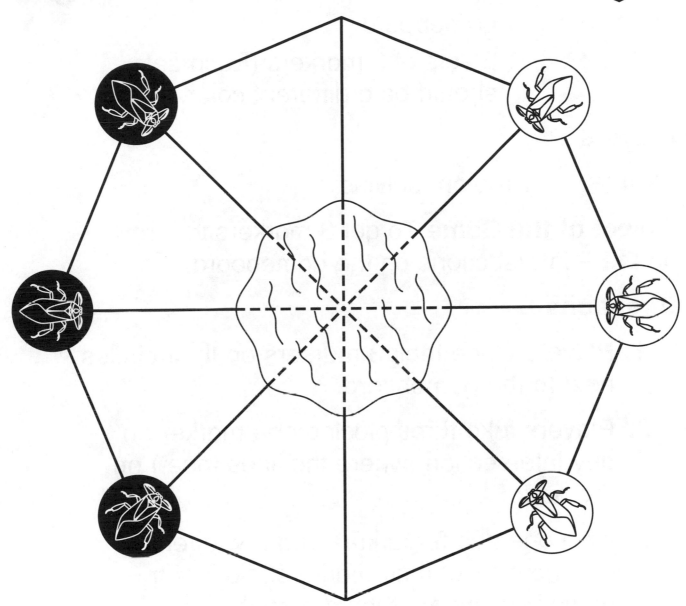

PROJECT 3 | **Nine Holes Directions**

Materials ☐ gameboard

☐ 2 sets of 3 markers (Each set should be a different color.)

Players   2

Skill   Problem-solving

Object of the Game To get 3 markers in a row on the 9 intersections on the gameboard.

Directions

1. Players place their 3 markers on their circles next to the gameboard.

2. Players take turns placing one marker on any intersection (where the lines meet) on the board.

3. If no one has 3 markers in a row after placing all 3 of their markers, players try again from where they are on the board. They take turns moving one marker at a time from one intersection to an open intersection next to it.

4. The game is tied if no one can get 3 in a row.

PROJECT 3 | **Nine Holes Gameboard**

Player 1

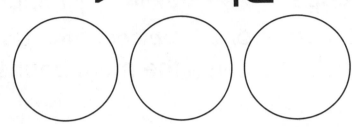

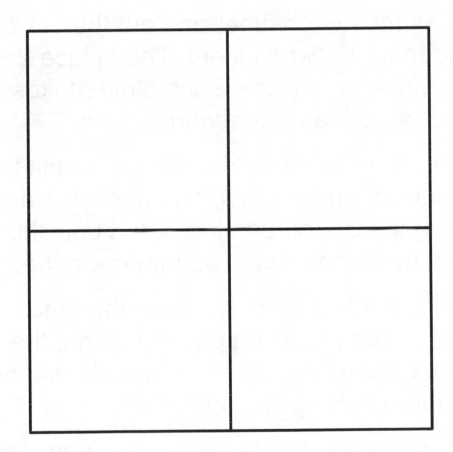

Player 2

Owari Directions

Materials
☐ gameboard
☐ 2 cups
☐ 16 beans or small counters

Players 2

Skill Problem-solving

Object of the Game To collect the most beans

Directions

1. Players face each other and put the gameboard between them. They place 2 beans in each square. Each player takes a cup to store his or her beans.

2. Players take turns picking up the beans from any square on their side and placing 1 bean in each square around the board until the beans from the chosen square are gone.

3. If a player's last bean lands on the other player's side in a square with 1 bean, the player whose turn it is takes both beans and puts them in his or her cup.

4. Play continues until there are no beans left on one side of the board.

5. The winner is the player with the most beans.

PROJECT 3

Owari Gameboard

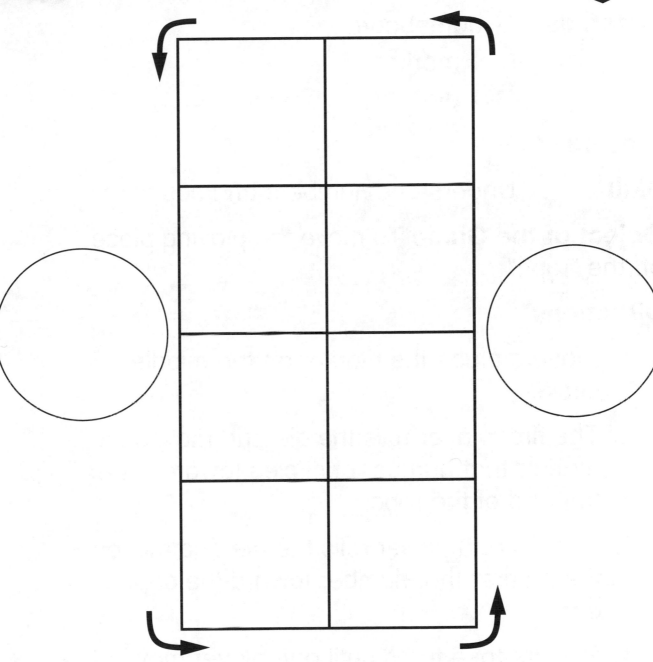

PROJECT 3 | **Tug of War Directions**

Materials   ☐ gameboard
  ☐ 1 marker
  ☐ 1 die

Players   2

Skill   Understand numbers and counting

Object of the Game To move the playing piece off the "rope"

Directions

1. Players place the marker on the middle circle.

2. The first player rolls the die and moves the marker that number of circles toward his or her end of the rope.

3. The second player rolls the die and moves the marker that number toward the opposite end.

4. Players take turns until one player moves the marker off the rope.

PROJECT 3

Tug of War Gameboard

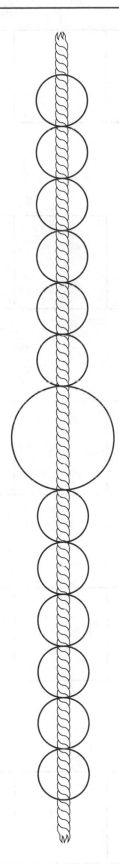

PROJECT 3

Blank Gameboard

End

Start

PROJECT 4

Measuring Tools Pictures

1 cup

$\frac{1}{2}$ cup

$\frac{1}{4}$ cup

1 tablespoon

1 teaspoon

PROJECT 4

Measuring Tools Pictures *continued*

1 cup

$\frac{1}{3}$ cup

$\frac{1}{2}$ cup

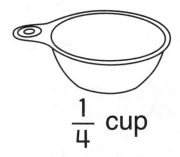

$\frac{1}{4}$ cup

78

PROJECT 6 | Mapping a Room

Make a map of a room where you spend lots of time. Use the back of this paper as your map. You will need tape or glue to attach the rectangle your teacher gave you.

1. First, draw any doors and windows.

2. Then, attach the cutout rectangle to show an important thing in the room, such as a bed, a table, or a sofa.

3. Add other furniture and objects that are in the room. (You can draw them or attach cutout paper shapes.)

4. Label some of the things on your map.

5. Bring your room map to school to share with the class.

Routine Masters

Name _____ Date _____

ROUTINE 2 | **Attendance Sign-In Sheet**

Week of _____					
Name	M	T	W	Th	F

83

Name _____ Date _____

ROUTINE 3 | **Job Chart Cards**

Weather

Temperature

Daily Schedule

SEPTEMBER

S	M	T	W	T	F	S
	1	2	3	4	5	6
7	8	9	10	11	12	13
14	15	16	17	18	19	20
21	22	23	24	25	26	27
28	29	30				

Calendar

Today's Attendance

_____ children are in our class.

_____ children are PRESENT.

_____ children are ABSENT.

Attendance

0 1 2 3 4 5

Number of the Day

84

Routine Masters

ROUTINE 2 | **Attendance Record Slip**

Today's Attendance

_____ children are in our class.

_____ children are PRESENT.

_____ children are ABSENT.

Today's Attendance

_____ children are in our class.

_____ children are PRESENT.

_____ children are ABSENT.

ROUTINE 2

Attendance Sign-In Sheet

Week of _____	M	T	W	Th	F
Name					

ROUTINE 3 | **Job Chart Cards**

Weather

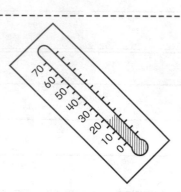

Temperature

Daily Schedule

SEPTEMBER						
S	M	T	W	T	F	S
	1	2	3	4	5	6
7	8	9	10	11	12	13
14	15	16	17	18	19	20
21	22	23	24	25	26	27
28	29	30				

Calendar

Today's Attendance

_____ children are in our class.

_____ children are PRESENT.

_____ children are ABSENT.

Attendance

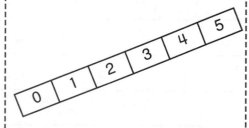

Number of the Day

ROUTINE 3

Job Chart Cards *continued*

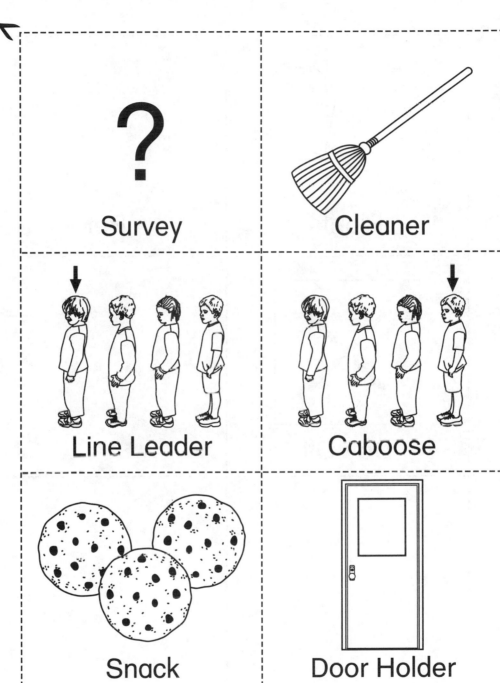

Survey

Cleaner

Line Leader

Caboose

Snack

Door Holder

ROUTINE 3 | **Job Chart Cards** *continued*

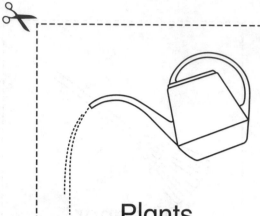

Plants

Pet

Day Off

ROUTINE 6 | **Weather Symbol Cards**

Sunny

Cloudy

Rainy

Snowy

Partly Cloudy

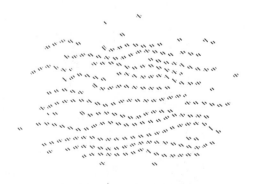

Foggy

ROUTINE 7

Clothes for Different Temperatures

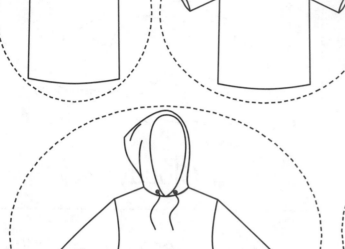

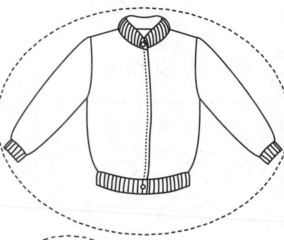

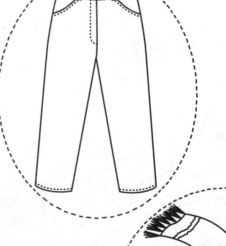

ROUTINE 8

Survey Tally Sheet

Survey Question

_____

_____

_____

Yes	No

Teaching Aid Masters

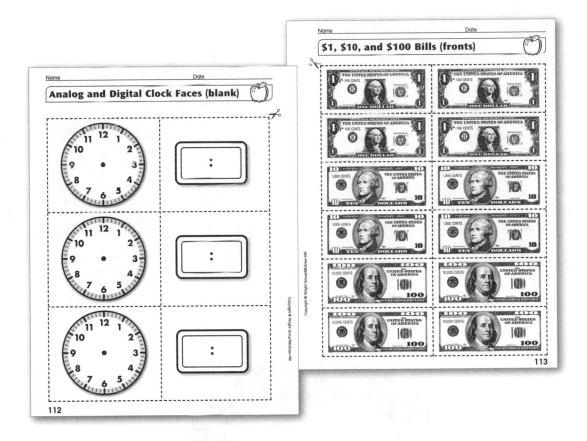

Large Number Card 0

Large Number Cards 1 and 2

Large Number Cards 3 and 4

94

Large Number Cards 5 and 6

Large Number Cards 7 and 8

Large Number Cards 9 and 10

Large Number Cards 11 and 12

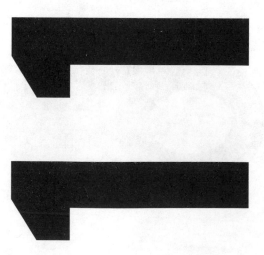

Large Number Cards 13 and 14

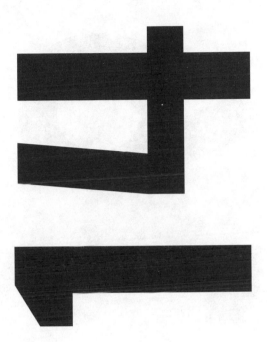

Large Number Cards 15 and 16

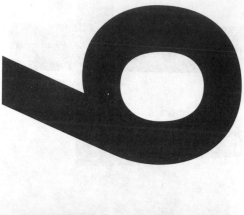

Large Number Cards 17 and 18

Large Number Cards 19 and 20

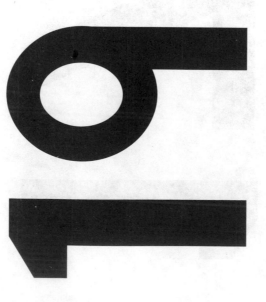

Ten Frame

Coins

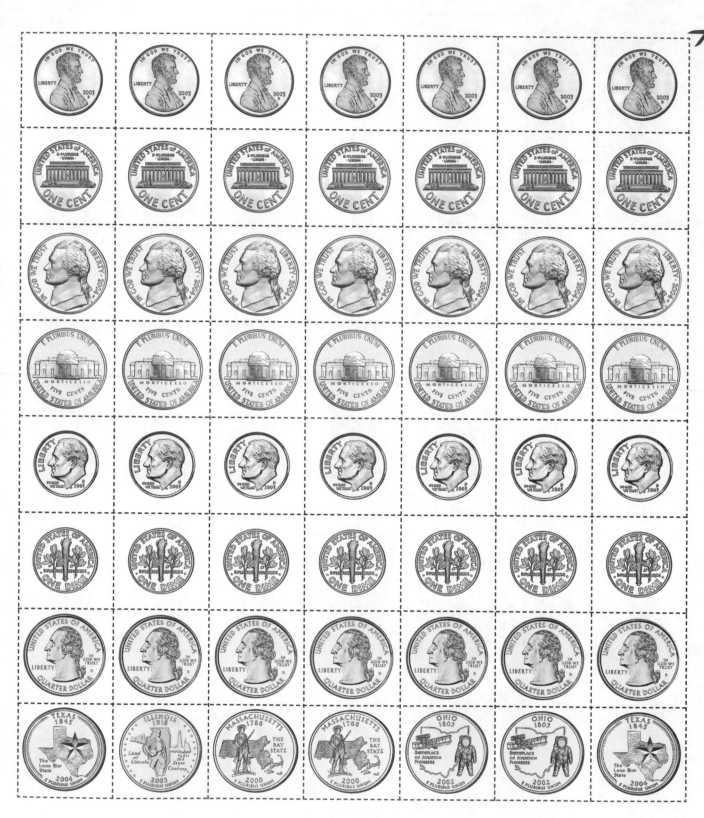

Small Number Cards (0–7)

0

4

1

5

2

6

3

7

Small Number Cards (8–15)

8

12

9

13

10

14

11

15

Small Number Cards (16–20)

16

17

18

19

20

Small Number Cards (blank)

Addition and Subtraction Symbols

Use these cards as you introduce the addition (+)
and subtraction (−) symbols.

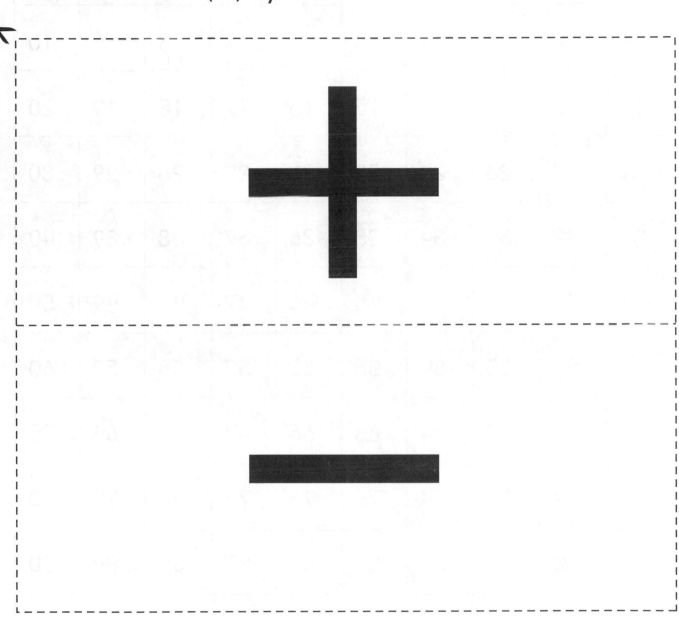

Small Number Grid

									0
1	2	3	4	5	6	7	8	9	10
11	12	13	14	15	16	17	18	19	20
21	22	23	24	25	26	27	28	29	30
31	32	33	34	35	36	37	38	39	40
41	42	43	44	45	46	47	48	49	50
51	52	53	54	55	56	57	58	59	60
61	62	63	64	65	66	67	68	69	70
71	72	73	74	75	76	77	78	79	80
81	82	83	84	85	86	87	88	89	90
91	92	93	94	95	96	97	98	99	100
101	102	103	104	105	106	107	108	109	110

Number Scroll

										1
										0

Analog and Digital Clock Faces (blank)

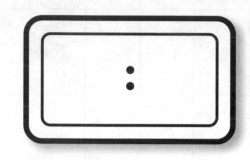

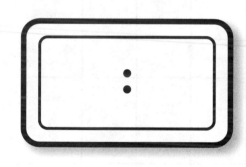

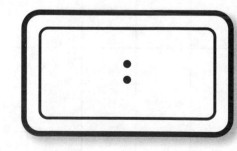

$1, $10, and $100 Bills (fronts)

$1, $10, and $100 Bills (backs)

✂ $1 Bills (fronts)

$1 Bills (backs)

Game Masters

Name _____ Date _____

Paper Money Exchange Game Directions

Materials
- ☐ 1 game mat per player (page 132)
- ☐ 1 cube marked $1 on 2 sides, $5 on 2 sides, and $10 on 2 sides
- ☐ bank of money: ten $1 bills and ten $10 bills per player
- ☐ one $100 bill

Players   2 or more

Skill   Recognize and exchange $1, $10, and $100 bills

Object of the Game To exchange ten $10 bills for the $100 bill

Directions

1. On each turn, a player rolls the cube and takes the correct bill (or combination of bills) from the bank. (For example, players can take five $1 bills when they roll $5.)

2. Players count their money after each turn.

3. When a player has ten $1 bills, he or she exchanges them for one $10 bill. When a player has ten $10 bills, he or she exchanges them for one $100 bill.

4. The game ends when a player exchanges ten $10 bills for the $100 bill.

131

Name _____ Date _____

Go Forward, Back Up Gameboard

Materials
- ☐ Two cubes: one numbered 0–5; one with 4 sides marked with a + symbol and colored green and 2 sides marked with a − symbol and colored red.

Players   2

Skill   Explore addition and subtraction

Object of the Game To reach the end of the path

Directions Players take turns rolling both cubes and moving ahead (+) or back (−) the correct number of spaces.

Start → [ ][ ][ ][ ][ ]

[ ][ ][ ][ ][ ]

[ ][ ][ ][ ][ ]

[ ][ ][ ][ ][ ] End

124

Attribute Spinner Game Spinners

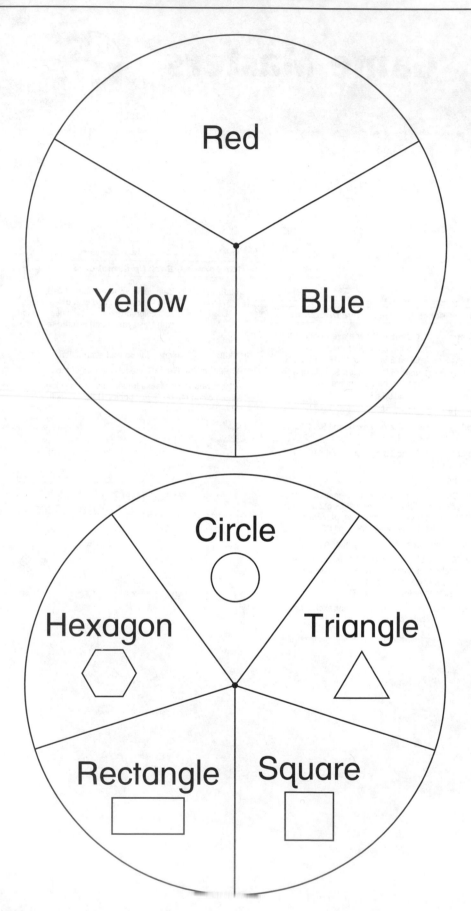

Attribute Spinner Game Spinners *continued*

LARGE   small

small   LARGE

thin   THICK

THICK   thin

Cover Half Directions and Gameboard

Materials ☐ 1 gameboard

☐ 1 die marked
1, 2, 3, 1, 2, 3

☐ 8 counters

Players 2

Skill Recognize halves

Object of the Game Work together to cover half of the gameboard

Directions

1. Partners take turns rolling the specially marked die.

2. Players place 1, 2, or 3 counters on the gameboard, depending on the roll of the die.

3. The game ends when half of the gameboard is covered.

Domino Concentration Cards

Domino Concentration Cards *continued*

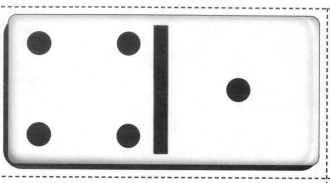

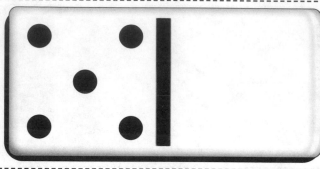

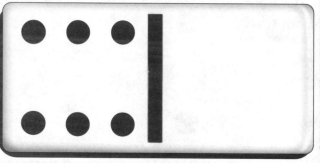

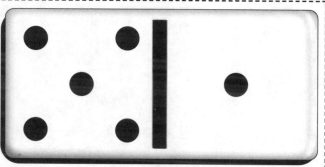

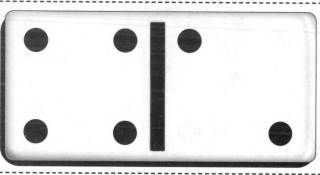

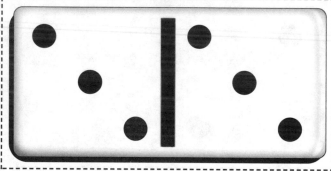

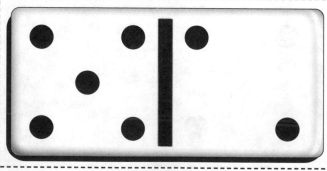

Domino Concentration Cards *continued*

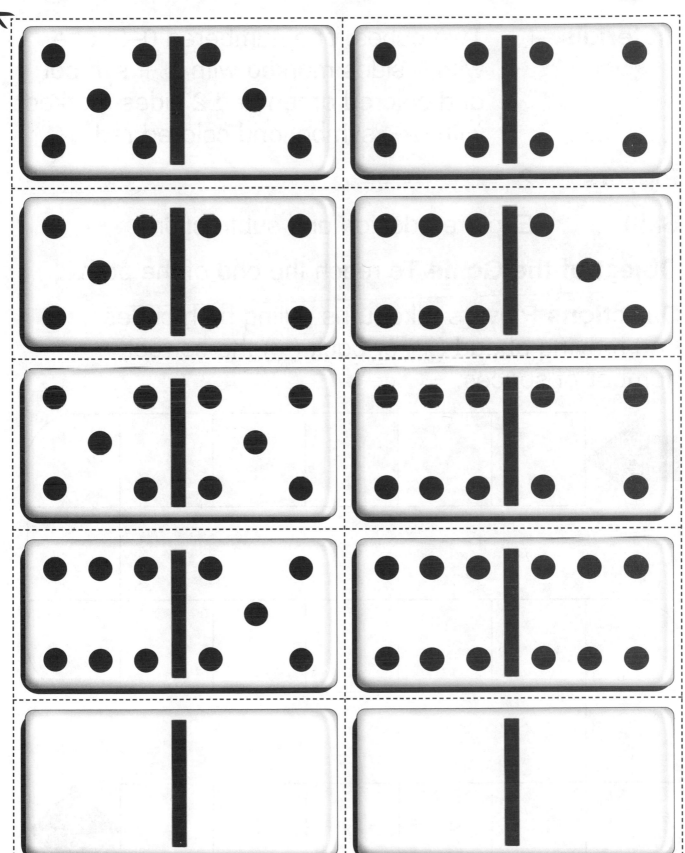

Go Forward, Back Up Gameboard

Materials ☐ Two cubes: one numbered 0–5; one with 4 sides marked with a + symbol and colored green and 2 sides marked with a − symbol and colored red.

Players 2

Skill Explore addition and subtraction

Object of the Game To reach the end of the path

Directions Players take turns rolling both cubes and moving ahead (+) or back (−) the correct number of spaces.

Start →

End

Money Grid Gameboard

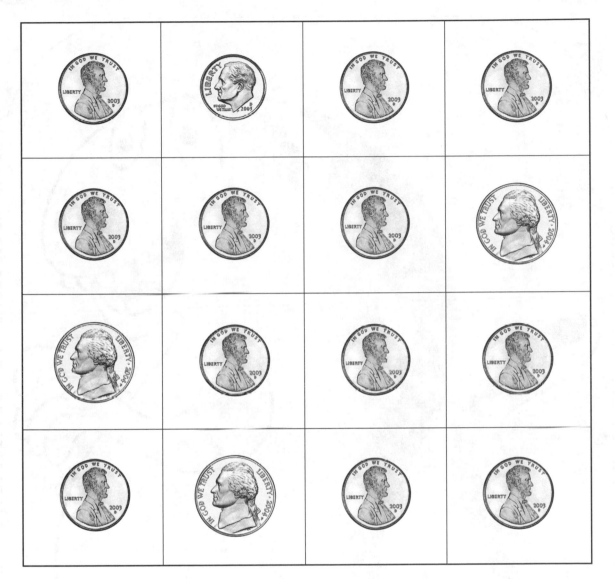

Monster Squeeze Monster (left side)

Monster Squeeze Monster (right side)

Monster Squeeze Mini Version

1	2	3	4	5	6	7	8	9	10

128

Number-Grid Game Directions

Materials □ Small Number Grid, *Math Masters,* p. 110

□ 1 scoring table

□ 1 die

□ 1 counter per player

Players 2 to 4

Skill To count and navigate on the number grid

Object of the Game Reach 100 on the number grid

Directions

1. Each player chooses a different-colored counter and places it on 0 on the number grid.

2. Taking turns, players roll a die and use the scoring table to see how many spaces to move their counters.

3. The first player to reach 100 is the winner.

Rolls	Spaces
•	1 or 10
•• (2)	2 or 20
••• (3)	3
•••• (4)	4
••••• (5)	5
•••••• (6)	6

Ones, Tens, Hundreds Game **Record Sheet**

Record how many single sticks, small bundles, and big bundles you have at the end of the *Ones, Tens, Hundreds Game.*

Big Bundles 100s	Bundles 10s	Single Sticks 1s

How many sticks did you collect all together?

_____

Paper Money Exchange Game Directions

Materials
- ☐ 1 game mat per player (page 132)
- ☐ 1 cube marked $1 on 2 sides, $5 on 2 sides, and $10 on 2 sides
- ☐ bank of money: ten $1 bills and ten $10 bills per player
- ☐ one $100 bill

Players   2 or more

Skill   Recognize and exchange $1, $10, and $100 bills

Object of the Game To exchange ten $10 bills for the $100 bill

Directions

1. On each turn, a player rolls the cube and takes the correct bill (or combination of bills) from the bank. (For example, players can take five $1 bills when they roll $5.)

2. Players count their money after each turn.

3. When a player has ten $1 bills, he or she exchanges them for one $10 bill. When a player has ten $10 bills, he or she exchanges them for one $100 bill.

4. The game ends when a player exchanges ten $10 bills for the $100 bill.

Paper Money Exchange Game Mat

$1 bills

$10 bills

$100 bills

Paper Money Exchange Game (Advanced)

Materials
- ☐ 1 game mat per player (page 132)
- ☐ 1 cube marked $1 on 2 sides, $5 on 2 sides, and $10 on 2 sides
- ☐ 1 cube marked $10 on 4 sides and $100 on 2 sides
- ☐ bank of money: ten $1 bills, ten $10 bills, and ten $100 bills per player
- ☐ $1,000 Bank Draft (page 134)

Players 2 or more

Skill Recognize and exchange bills up to $1,000

Object of the Game To exchange ten $100 bills for the $1,000 Bank Draft

Directions

1. On each turn, a player rolls the cubes and takes the correct bills from the bank.

2. When a player has ten $1 bills, he or she exchanges them for one $10 bill. When a player has ten $10 bills, he or she exchanges them for one $100 bill.

3. The game ends when a player exchanges ten $100 bills for the $1,000 Bank Draft.

Paper Money Exchange Game (Advanced) Bank Draft

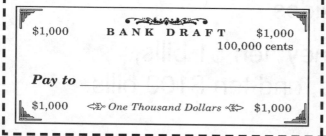
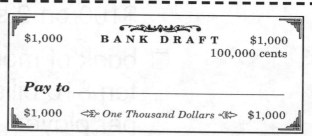

$1,000	**B A N K D R A F T**	$1,000
		100,000 cents
Pay to _____		
$1,000	❄ *One Thousand Dollars* ❄	$1,000

Plus or Minus Game Gameboards

135

Spin a Number (1–10) Gameboard

End

Start

Teen Frame Gameboard

Teen Frame Ten Strips

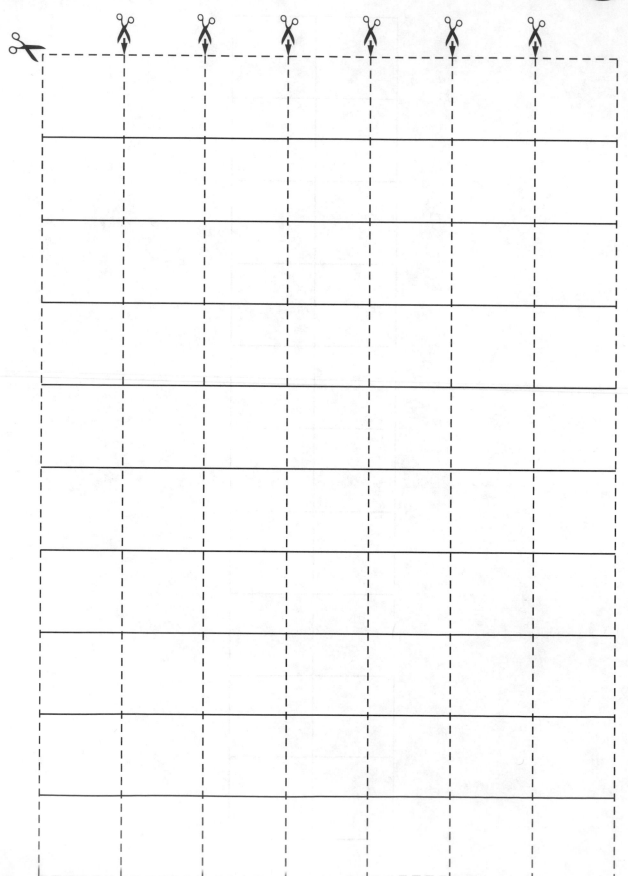

Teen Tangle (11–20) Spinner

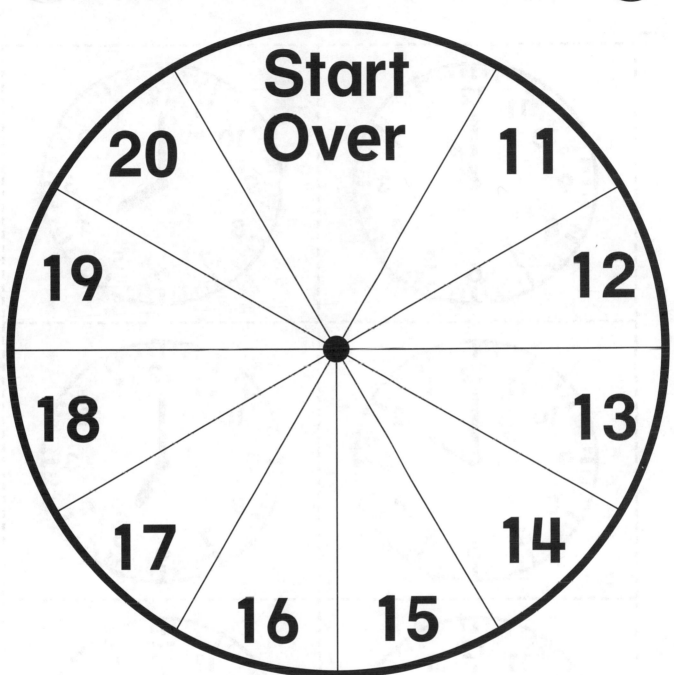

Time Match **Cards**

Time Match Cards *continued*

Time Match Cards *continued*

Time Match Cards *continued*